Einstein's Predicament

Einstein's Predicament

A New Approach to the Speed of Light

by

Francis Pym and Clifford Denton

Twoedged Sword Publications

First published 2005

ISBN-13   978-1-905447-06-0

ISBN-10   1-905447-06-X

Twoedged Sword Publications
PO Box 266, Waterlooville, PO7 5ZT
www.twoedgedswordpublications.co.uk

Acknowledgements

Francis Pym

There are so many to whom I owe so much in the preparation of the material for this book. Years ago my wife had been to a jumble sale and found a Pelican book entitled *Relativity for the Layman* (James A Coleman, William-Frederick Press, New York, 1954) knowing I was interested in the subject. This was seminal: I was struck by what I saw as the serious illogicallity of the book's arguments and immediately began to think of an alternative with little idea of how to formulate it or how to make contact with useful academic establishments. Eventually in the '60s I met Tim Clark, a student at Imperial College, London, and his tutor. I was most grateful when they took up my ideas for his post graduate thesis helping to draw up basic assumptions and motion rules. These were applicable to a spatial light-carrying medium but still with Relativity problems. Later, I was introduced to Dr Lindsay Douglas. I am indebted to him for his inspiration, rewriting, quick assessment, encouragement, amazement at the whole picture, and for his contacts with Dr Adrian Otterwill and others at the Dept of Mathematics, Magdalene College, Oxford.

Then I met Dr Clifford Denton without whom I could have made very little progress in bypassing Relativity Theory. His belief in what we were doing was very important, as was our bond and our untiring tenacity in searching together for the truth. He pressed for progress using logical 'engineering' procedures taking one step at a time in order to express the emerging 'architectural' notions in a language that made sense, with of course the loyal support of his wife Christine.

I also express my thanks to the Trustees of the Joshua Trust for their interest, encouragement and support; to Dr Peter Senior of Loughborough University for his interest and helpful corrections and for introducing Cellular Automata; to Jonathan Stigant, of Texas USA, of Satellite Assisted Surveying, for his encouragement; to Mrs Rosabel Topalian for her role as a prudent teacher of physics in guiding our thoughts and correcting elementary mistakes; to Dr David and Joan Rosevear for their support and for inviting me to lecture at one of their European Conferences; to Professor Andrew McIntosh, University of Leeds, for his appreciation of the value of the enterprise; to Mrs Olga Marshall for her hospitality, understanding and wisdom during conferences; to Dr Peter Holmes for encouragement to persist in reaching out into the academic world; to Guy Hoghton for his interest and help in checking our ideas; to David Firth for his electrical engineering skills with experiments; and for Alan Rose, Christian Puritz, and Evert van de Heidi for their not so favourable but nevertheless practical and useful critical analyses.

I am grateful to our son John for his aptitude with equations and for his professional civil engineering skills, for sharing and contributing his own ideas for experiments using cogs, lights and wires etc.; our daughters Rebekah and Victoria who were curiously interested and made helpful suggestions; Gordon and Hugh Battye who helped in my struggles with the most elementary algebra and physics, as well as many others who read the material and saw that what we were trying to do might make sense. Our thanks also go to our interested and patient publisher Paul Rose of Twoedged Sword Publications, introduced to us by Mike Phelan.

Last of all but by no means least I acknowledge with precious thanks, my wife Marigold for her loving support over a long period when she could not have understood much of what we were doing; for helping with our English, grammar, spelling, proof reading and so on, and most of all for JCOL.

Francis Pym
October 2005

Clifford Denton

I am grateful to have studied mathematics and physics in an age where absolute frames of reference were assumed, being then able to study the basic principles of Relativity Theory from this perspective. It gave me a caution when approaching theories which promised much but seemed to expect too much of a mindset change to accept them wholesale.

My first acknowledgements, therefore, go to my teachers who cultivated an interest in the laws of Physics and the tools of Mathematics, so setting a firm foundation in my academic life. For those born into an age of relative thinking, I would propose that they do not know what they are missing, compared with those of us with a secure framework cultivated from absolute principals in law and morals. It is for this reason that I have desired to understand the workings of the universe and, since meeting my colleague Francis Pym, of investigating what we perceived as the errors of Relativity Theory.

In our partnership, I have gained immense respect for the tenacity of Francis in not giving up and so keeping this project alive. Put a mathematician together with an architect and there is both the potential for what we have now achieved or the potential for sleepless nights due to the different means of communication. We have wrestled with how to express ideas, borne mainly from intuitive concepts, into mathematical language, albeit that the mathematical tools used were not complex. I greatly acknowledge the contribution of Francis to keep this project alive and to see it through to completion.

The concepts we have wrestled with did not require complex mathematics but they—the concepts themselves—are not as easy to grasp as we would have hoped. We needed to enter the mindset of relativity in order to seek to correct it, and this is something that our readers will have to face too. I have also greatly valued the many interactions that have taken place in the home of Francis and Marigold, the hospitality, the discussions on other topics of Christian apologetics, and the environment of faith and prayer that we find there.

Finally, for my part there is the acknowledgement of encouragement from others of our family and friends who have shown interest in the end results of our investigations, who never quite understood nor believed in Relativity Theory, but couldn't say why. It is to these that we now offer this book.

Clifford Denton
October 2005

Contents

1

Concepts

Assumptions and their Consequences

A hundred years ago Einstein published a foundational paper on the subject of light that has largely been accepted as a working document in the scientific world until now, even though it has been found incompatible with other theories. Most people do not have the scientific background either to understand or to challenge Einstein's papers and have had to put their trust in scientists. Yet, with some simple maths we plan in this book to demonstrate that Einstein may have made some serious errors. These errors are not so much within the development of his papers, as in the foundational assumptions that were made. Therefore, we are seeking to look at the logical implications of bypassing Einstein's theory of relativity which, if we are honest, no one completely understands.

Many people are not trained as scientists so might assume that eminent scientists discover truth. However, the truth of scientific discovery is only as valid as the truth of the founding principles and assumptions. Science such as physics is concerned with observation, experimentation, measurements, framing of theories and predictions, but these things are not examined in isolation. Every scientific conclusion depends on basic assumptions in just the same way that each branch of philosophy depends on foundational assumptions. Scientific and philosophical logic is of the kind; 'if A is true and B is true then we can conclude that C is true'. Science has experimental or mathematical logic to support it so that it can deal with the real world rather than just ideas, as is done in philosophy, though the two disciplines are converging in our day. For Einstein, the assumptions of Relativity Theory were based on the speed of light.

An informed layman with school level maths should be able to follow our reasoning in the rest of the book. However, we would point out that though the mathematics is straightforward the concepts could be quite difficult, so that the book will need to be read and thought through very carefully. This explanatory chapter therefore sets out the main ideas in a more popular manner without the use of mathematics, as a help to the less confident readers, though the remaining chapters may broadly be understood by skipping the maths.

History

Prior to Einstein there had been the idea that the universe was filled with a motionless substance or background medium that was called the Ether. Its characteristics in the universe were found hard to assess and its presence hard to detect. However, in this book we introduce a new term for this background medium. We will use the term *Fixed Frame of Reference* (or FFR) rather than *Ether* for technical reasons, but for simplicity in this chapter we will retain the term *Ether* for the background medium.

When serious consideration was being given to the existence of the Ether it was thought that light travelled through it in waves. However, detection of these waves was not easy. With sound waves, we can detect them as they travel through the air, but it has not been possible to either detect the Ether or monitor the travel of light waves through it in the same way. This is largely because light travels faster than anything else and this makes experiments difficult.

If the Ether exists, then it is the substance *within* and *between* the physical elements of the universe that interests us, but we do not have instruments to measure it or vessels to contain it. If it exists, atoms of the universe will interact with the Ether as they move through it. Since these are the smallest constituents of matter, we cannot have instruments small enough to make observations or measurements at that level. Thus, we have to make assumptions.

The problem that scientists such as Einstein faced was that there seemed to be a very strange result when attempts were made to measure not only the speed of the earth through the Ether but also the speed of light itself. This was not like measuring the speed of sound.

Suppose a vehicle transmits sound waves as it moves. To an observer travelling with the vehicle, the sound transmitted in front will be measured as being slower than when measured by someone who is stationary on the ground. For example, an aeroplane can go at such a rate through the air that it can sometimes exceed the speed of its own sound. Usually a person on the ground will hear the sound of a plane as it passes by, and for a fast plane, its sound appears to come from behind.

For a straightforward situation in a moving vehicle, a person measuring his own sound subtracts the velocity of the vehicle from that of its sound to obtain its apparent velocity.

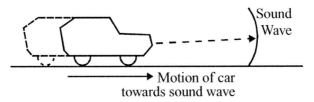

Motion of car
towards sound wave

This did not seem the same for light waves. Whether a body was moving or not, it seemed from the experiments that had been carried out that no subtraction was necessary. Whether moving or not, everyone seemed to get the same answer for the speed of light. This result naturally cast doubt on the existence of the Ether as well as establishing a philosophical problem for scientists. When Einstein began to think about this problem, he proposed that it was possible to avoid it and set out to get round it, in a sense by ignoring it.

To him it was not necessary to refer to a universe that was at absolute rest. If the Ether could be detected it was thought that it would define the state of absolute rest. Since the Ether could not be detected, Einstein *assumed* that by using a new system of relative measurements he could ignore it, so he abandoned the absolute measurements that would have been related to the Ether. Secondly, since the speed of light always *seemed* to be measured as constant whatever the motion of an object through the universe, Einstein established this as the other foundational *assumption* of his Relativity Theory.

While Einstein was able to make great and convincing strides forward, the consequences were that physical quantities then needed redefinition. For example, time became a relative concept, with time changing as a body moved, no longer relying on absolute measurements. Scientists are at liberty to make new definitions that are consistent with the theories, but they also have to bear the consequences. One major consequence of Einstein's theory is the loss of absolute measurements.

That said, there is not only the spread of relativity theory into other areas of philosophy but also into the conscience of mankind and the whole area of relative morals. Moreover, there can also be errors in having wrong assumptions that are then carried forward into other major areas of science.

Passage of Light Through Space

We propose that one major error lies in the assumption that light travels at the same constant speed to every observer. As we have said, measurement of the speed of light is not as straightforward as the measurement of the speed of sound. This is because of its immense rapidity and because nothing is known to travel at a greater speed. This means that when we send out a light ray it is impossible physically to keep up with it to see how fast it travels.

One might be tempted to think that the way to overcome this would be to set up an experiment. Suppose a light signal were sent out from a source at point A to be received at point B at a known distance. One could then determine the time of travel in the same way that one would calculate the speed of sound in air leading to a calculation of the speed of light.

However, herein lies a fallacy. One needs to be able to synchronise clocks at A and B first. How can one do this? Either one puts the clocks together and synchronises them before moving them apart, or one sends a signal from A to B so that the clock at B is set to the time at A. We cannot be sure that either of these methods works.

In the first case, when we move the clocks apart, we are not sure if the movement of the clock from A to B changes its time. In fact, as we explain below, we do believe that this can be so. In the second case, the signal that we would send from A to B to synchronise the clocks would have to be transmitted by an electromagnetic signal at a known speed. This would be at the speed of light— the very thing we are trying to measure.

Thus, every scientific experiment to measure the speed of light has relied on a different approach from this. In these experiments, light is sent from a transmitter at A to a reflector at B and back, while the light is timed over the double journey. The point is that all attempts to measure the speed of light that have produced useable results, give an *average speed for this double journey* <u>rather than an actual measurement of the speed of light in one direction.</u>

Let us take an analogy from the measurement of the speed of sound in air. Suppose a vehicle is travelling towards a distant wall at a certain speed and sends out a sound wave carried in still air.

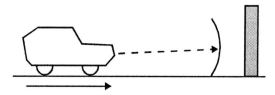

The sound travels in the air and the vehicle moves a certain distance before the sound reaches the wall and the echo returns. The speed of sound on the outward journey as measured from the vehicle is the actual speed of sound in still air *minus* the speed of the vehicle.

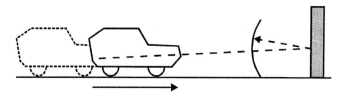

On the return journey, since the vehicle is moving towards the echo, the apparent speed of sound will be the speed of sound in still air *plus* the speed of the vehicle.

If both the vehicle *and* the reflecting wall moved at the same speed, maintaining the distance between them or if there were a head wind, the effect would be amplified. In this case, we could have calculated the average speed of sound by dividing the 2-way distance by the total time. Again, we would not have taken account of the fact that, measured in the vehicle, the sound travelled at a different speed in each of the two directions, i.e. to the wall and back.

Now, this is a point that has never been refuted even in Einstein's Theory of Relativity. If light travels like sound in the medium (the Ether), as we propose, then light too travels at a different speed in each of the two directions. If the light source and reflector, A and B, are travelling together through the medium there will be different speeds to and from the reflector that are 'averaged out' when a calculation is made of the 2-way journey. The problem here is that in the case of the measurement of the speed of light we cannot make the two separate measurements to and from the reflector and so detect if there is an error in our assumption.

However, we do show a simple calculation later in the following chapters that gives a remarkable result in the case of the measurement of the speed of light for a 2-way journey from source A to reflector B and back. If A and B are moving at any speed through the medium then we always get the same 'average' speed for light for the double journey even though the speeds of light to and from the reflector are themselves different. Thus Einstein's assumption *seems* correct, but it is only correct for an averaged 2-way passage of light. Moreover, this result cannot be used to infer (as it is in modern science) that light always travels at the same speed whether the instrument is moving through the universe or not.

Such suppositions have important consequences when we consider light from distant stars moving with respect to us, since the stars themselves are moving as well. Later, when we come to consider the age and development of the universe, assumptions about the speed of light have major implications. One such of course is the contribution this has to the theory that the universe began with a 'Big Bang'.

Einstein's assumption about the speed of light allowed him to proceed with the Theory of Relativity which then became a self-contained mathematical system. To proceed with his theory other issues needed reinterpretation, for instance the measurement of length and time in a moving body. In practice, the equations of Special Relativity relate to bodies moving at very high constant speeds requiring that time slows and lengths shorten as a body moves. They start with the assumption that light always travels in any direction at the same speed according to any observer. Conclusions about change of time and length followed afterwards.

Concern

We argue the case differently. We are very concerned about Einstein's relative measurements in his view of the universe and at the loss of absolute measurements. To Einstein, instruments in each body (space ships, planets, the earth, the sun or stars, for example) make all measurements relative to the body in which they are located, with no reference to any absolute measurements. Each body in the universe, to Einstein, is like its own world unto itself with no need to refer to a set of absolutes that must be defined in some way. His theory came about because of the inability of scientists to detect the Ether that would define the position of an absolute rest in the universe from which all absolute measurements could be made. However, in abandoning the concept of absolute rest, one's concept of the universe changes too.

We propose a return to the concept of absolute rest and absolute reference for time and length. This is even though the Ether has not and probably cannot be detected. The issue here is truth. If we cannot detect the Ether, this is no reason to ignore the possibility of its existence. In the end such theories as Relativity Theory introduced confusing paradoxes and mystical ideas about the universe compared with logical alternatives based on the return to absolutes.

There is therefore a reasonable case for leaving the Theory of Relativity and building afresh on absolutes. Of course, we still need to deal with such issues as slowing of time and shortening of lengths. We show later that shortening of lengths can be explained in a different way. We propose that the speed of forces between molecules, that hold matter together, varies in relation to the speed that the matter travels through the ether. It is this variation of the speed of forces that changes lengths. In regard to time, we would simply state that it is not *time* that changes with motion. It is the rate at which *clocks* record the passage of time that changes due to the motion of the matter itself.

Simultaneity

The final important point to raise in this chapter is the notion of something called 'Simultaneity'. To proceed with his theories, and knowing the impossibility of synchronising clocks at two different points, A and B, since one has to send a signal from A to B to do this, Einstein cleverly bypassed the problem. He used the word 'Synchronicity' instead of 'Simultaneity' and *defined* this term for the purposes of his new theory. He could not solve the problem of Simultaneity so defined himself out of the problem! Even if two events in relation to absolute measurements in the universe did *not* occur at the same time in relation to absolute measurements, Einstein could still *define* them as 'synchronous' according to his theory.

Remarkably, in spite of redefining certain issues such as time and simultaneity and failing to disprove the existence of a background medium in the universe, Einstein's theory has held ground for a hundred years. We suggest therefore, that it is now timely to challenge this approach through the return to absolutes, and hold out the possibility of returning to this more easily understood basis of measurement in the universe.

2

Proposal

In this book, we reconsider the passage of light with respect to what we will call a Fixed Frame of Reference (FFR) at absolute rest in the universe. Was Einstein right in his supposition that some sort of physical matrix or FFR in space can be ignored without consequences? He redefined certain issues including time and simultaneity in order to proceed with his Theory of Special Relativity (SR). This approach, though attractive, is not consistent with theories based on absolute measurements, and bears consequences that must not be neglected. By re-examining Einstein's second postulate in SR, we propose that an FFR is plausible, although its location may be uncertain. In reopening this route of inquiry, we suggest a return to the basis of an FFR model and to the investigation of the original meaning of time within a universe of absolutes.

To do this we reconsider some of the foundational issues addressed in the early papers on SR. We then open the way for an alternative model, showing that the prevalence of an FFR is consistent with experimental results that caused its neglect in the derivation of SR. The authors do not dispute that the results of SR have been outstanding as far as advance in science is concerned. We propose that the valid results of SR can be confirmed in a new theory of absolutes, but that invalid results must be corrected.

Relativity

Towards the end of the 19th century, scientists faced a dilemma. All attempts had failed to detect an 'aether' or 'ether' in space in which light was thought to travel. Until this dilemma could be resolved or until an alternative route of scientific enquiry could open up, it seemed that progress in understanding the motion of physical bodies would be withheld. In 1905, Einstein's elegant paper, *On the Electrodynamics of Moving Bodies,*[1] broke open a new avenue of thinking and the Theory of Relativity was born. From such a simple starting point, immense strides took place in physics. However, after a hundred years we have come to a new set of dilemmas. While relativity is the standard model for understanding the universe today, Relativity and Quantum Theories still seem incompatible. Rather than going back to re-examine the departure point of a century ago, relativistic concepts are still being included in new theories, such as various String Theories.

By its very nature, relativity is illogical as it forgoes the need for certain absolutes in the universe. This has considerable implications for the mindset of our modern day, impinging on philosophy and moral law as well as physics. It also has a bearing on how mankind views the origin of the universe, contributing directly to the idea of a 'Big Bang' versus that which was not by natural means. If relativity is to be retained, a theory such as String Theory has to be imposed, which incorporates concepts of eleven dimensions of space, parallel universes and so on.

When surveying some of the end products of relativity and looking at the propositions of new theories such as these, one might wonder if it might not be better to make a fresh study of the concept of an FFR. In many eyes, returning to the point of departure of 1905 would seem to be a step back. However, let us see if such a step is indeed a step back.

3

Point of Departure

Since 1887, the best known and very accurate experiment by Michelson and Morley[2] (MM) to detect the speed of the earth as it moves through an 'ether' has been repeated many times. A light beam from a source is divided into two rays propagating at right angles to each other, making them travel set distances to mirrors where each is reflected back. Interference patterns produced by the recombined light rays are expected to indicate a time difference that would detect the speed of the earth through this ether. This experiment constantly failed to detect its existence.

Material light ethers in space have never lacked critics. One of the dilemmas was the failure of the MM experiments. How could something exist that seemed undetectable or unaffected? Yet, all they had to do was to punch a brick back and forth in the hand to experience the resistance of such a material. The authors are proposing such a material at rest in what we have called the FFR, a concept similar to the ether. Thus, if we return to the point of departure, we will find that the hypothesis of an FFR is remarkably productive [3].

Nevertheless, the genius of Einstein's new theory lay in a point of departure from this dilemma that seemingly did not need to take account of such an ether. It is crucial to recall here that *the foundations of SR neither accepted nor denied the existence of an ether.* Prior to Einstein, advance in physics was held up by lack of positive evidence for its existence. Einstein thought he could overcome this by devising a theory that did not depend on it. He therefore set up two assumptions[4] for his theory. The first raised to the level of postulate, that:

> 1) *"not only the phenomena of mechanics but also those of electrodynamics have no properties that correspond to the concept of absolute rest."*

This postulate carried the *assumption* that nothing would be lost in ignoring the light-bearing ether, *while not denying its existence.* The second postulate was,

> 2) *"that light always propagates in empty space with a definite velocity c that is independent of the state of motion of the emitting body."*[5]

Einstein saw that if the speed of light seemed always to be constant he could use the Lorentz Transformations to confirm it.

We repeat this important point, that *in neither of his two postulates did Einstein state that an ether did not exist.* He only accepted that *it could not be detected.* So he moved forward with his theory because *its existence* did not seem to be needed as a matter for study. We quote,

> *"The introduction of a 'light ether' will prove to be superfluous, inasmuch as the view to be developed here will not require a*

'space at absolute rest' endowed with special properties.'[6]

Since then, those who have believed in SR may have inadvertently overlooked this point and so ignored the inconsistencies in the logic of SR.

Specifically we can state that the application of the second postulate is not consistent with an ether or FFR. A theory based on the efficacy of an FFR leads to the recovery of the concept of a state of absolute rest[7] in the universe and the consequences of light travelling through a medium at absolute rest. From this we can then build up a view of the physics of the universe based on the use of the medium *whether we can detect it or not*. Furthermore, if any extrapolations of relativity theory unwittingly assume its non-existence, when it does exist, then errors can creep in. Indeed, if one of Einstein's postulates is wrong then there will undoubtedly also be false conclusions from it. By implication, of course, we are questioning the validity of the Lorentz Transformations[8].

Specific difficulties that we would attribute to SR and therefore to General Relativity would include singularities (matter having mass but no size), aspects of gravitation, and the concept of time. We would also include some issues relating to the age and size of the universe derived from an interpretation of the red shift and brightness of light from distant galaxies.

Our proposition is that Relativity Theory in addition to the mysteries that followed in its train should be replaced. The alternative would be to recover the hypothesis that when a body moves through space, and when it transmits light, this light is carried with respect to an FFR independent of that body. This is rather like sound that travels through the air separated from its source. All absolute motion is then defined from a rest position in the FFR.

Throughout this book, we consider phenomena relating to the passage of radiation from a classical perspective based on the hypothesis that an FFR itself defines the light. It has also been necessary that reference to SR has been made because of the widespread acceptance of the theory. The purpose in doing so is to draw contrasts between SR and the results of our theory of light. However, it must be said that our line of investigation would have still been the same if SR had not been invented, but of course more difficult. Our primary purpose, therefore, is to demonstrate the plausibility of our theory of light. We nevertheless show that although Einstein created problems through SR, certain results can still be upheld while some of his basic postulates are not supported by our proposal.

4

Einstein's Predicament

We will show in this section that Einstein's definition of 'Simultaneity' will not be consistent with our theory of light. This is because Einstein's supposition is that light travels at constant speed relative to an observer. He applied this principle to give the duration of light travelling between two clocks, and assumed the time for the outward and return journeys is the same. If this is not the case, as we propose, then his definition of Simultaneity is incomplete. Indeed, this leads to the view that he *redefined time rather than keeping to the conventional concepts of time measurements*, contributing eventually to the idea of contortion of space and time.

In his 1905 paper, Einstein proposed a definition of Simultaneity with a view to establishing the conjecture that not only the phenomena of mechanics but also that of electrodynamics have no properties that correspond to the concept of absolute rest. However, within his definition for Simultaneity lies a predicament, as we shall see.

Now, regarding Simultaneity, Einstein writes:[9]

> *"If there is a clock at point A in space, then an observer located at A can evaluate the time of events in the immediate vicinity of A by finding the position of the hands of the clocks that are simultaneous with these*

*events. If there is another clock at point B
that in all respects resembles the clock at
point A, then the time of events in the
immediate vicinity of B can be evaluated by
an observer at point B. But it is not possible
to compare the time of an event at A with
one at point B without further stipulation.
So far we have only evaluated an 'A time'
and a 'B time', but not a common time for
A and B. The latter can now be determined
by establishing by definition that the 'time'
for light to travel from A to B is equal to the
time it takes to travel from B to A. For,
suppose a ray of light that leaves from A for
B at 'A time' t_A, is reflected from B towards
A at 'B time' t_B, and arrives back at A at 'A
time' t'_A The two clocks are synchronous by
definition if*

$$t_B - t_A = t'_A - t_B \text{ "}$$

This *definition* of synchronicity then became the basis in
SR for time measurements in all 'frames of reference'.
We would propose that Einstein began to *redefine* time
and space at this point from relative quantities to an
invariant, or space-time interval, τ, and made it subject
to the concepts of SR[10]. If we are to re-establish our
confidence in an absolute frame of reference (the ether
or FFR determining the state of absolute rest), time once
more becomes an absolute quantity. This has immense
consequences for recovery from erroneous, sometimes
strange, hypotheses of SR.

Einstein further stipulates in his definition of Simultaneity[1] that

> *"Based on experience, we further stipulate that the quantity*

$$\frac{2\overline{AB}}{t'_A - t_A} = c$$

> *be a universal constant (the velocity of light in empty space)."*

Einstein assumed that the overall speed of light, as measured by a 2-way passage of signals from A to B, gives the value of the speed of light irrespective of any motion of the observer. *His proposal implies that the time for the outward and return journeys of a light signal between A and B are the same.* His conclusion is therefore theoretical and given without means of proof. This is because practical knowledge of the value of t_B is denied and ambiguity remains. Consequently, if a light carrying FFR is fundamental, and if the motion of A and B through it does influence the speed of light from A to B and B to A, then we propose that *Einstein chose a definition that does not hold.*

Specifically, the equation

$$\frac{2\overline{AB}}{t'_A - t_A} = c$$

does *not* take into account that in the FFR the time of the passage of light from A to B *can* be different from the passage of light travelling from B to A.

We therefore propose an alternative solution to the problem of light and synchronicity by examining the effect of motion on the measurement of time and length which, as we shall see, bypasses Relativity Theory.

5

The Effect of Motion on the Measurement of Time and Length

Proposition

In this section, we will consider time rate change [12] (or time dilation) and length decrease[13] in SR. These phenomena are familiar to SR. In SR they are a product of the Lorentz Transformations. However, we propose that these are physical realities resulting simply from the reaction of a body moving in an FFR. While lengths *actually* shrink and clocks *actually* slow, it is important to realise the difference from SR. Einstein *redefined time*. We propose that *measuring instruments of time* simply change.

Up to this point of departure, both Coulomb and Maxwell had begun serious studies of non-instantaneous transfer of radiation involving a commodity or dielectric. More recently, Quantum Theory has proposed that molecular systems are held in place by virtual quantum photons that bond over a period at the speed of light. We can picture photons travelling over molecular distances where time of travel is an important criterion. When a body moves through an FFR *the relative velocity of light changes as a result*. This causes time rate change and length decrease—both real physical effects—that we now illustrate using this change in the speed of light.

Passage of light in the FFR

We can illustrate a line of thought through a simple example on the assumption that ordinary matter depends on the properties of molecular bonding explained in terms of contributions from constituent molecules.

Suppose A, B, and C in the diagram below are three hypothetical centres of molecular bonding held in place in a solid body by these virtual photons. Consider absolute distance AC first. AC is at right angles to the direction of motion of the body that is moving through the FFR towards positions A_1 and C_1 at speed **v**. Due to this motion, the resultant speed of bonding photons apparent to the FFR is calculated from a right-angled triangle of velocities, AA_1C_1.

To instruments at rest in the FFR, the hypotenuse AC_1 of the triangle of velocities AC_1A_1 in the diagram represents the speed for the 2-way passage of photons at **c**. To those moving with centres A and C, it will be over the path A_1C_1 giving a resultant of their speed of,

$$\sqrt{c^2 - v^2},$$

i.e. slower than **c**. The resultant speed over distance A_1B_1 is defined further on page 55 ff.

Triangle of Velocities as seen from the FFR

'v' represents the velocity of centres of photon bonding at Ⓐ Ⓑ and Ⓒ moving right in the FFR through positions A_1, B_1 and C_1.

'c' represents the speed in the FFR over the mean path of photon bonding along the hypotenuse.

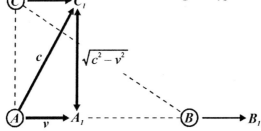

$\sqrt{c^2 - v^2}$ *represents the resultant bonding velocity of photons between A_1 and C_1 in the FFR triangle of velocities AC_1A_1.*

Now, the mean resultant velocity of photons between A_1 and C_1, $\sqrt{c^2 - v^2}$, may also be written with respect to c, as $\sqrt{c^2 - v^2} \times c/c$, or $\sqrt{1 - v^2/c^2} \times c$.

Since $\sqrt{1 - v^2/c^2}$ will be a frequently occurring factor that decreases as velocity increases, let it be termed ϕ. Photons whose speed limit in the FFR is c, would then be seen by instruments stationary in the FFR to travel at a slower speed [14] over the perpendicular distance A_1C_1 at a resultant bonding velocity of...

$$\phi c$$

Time Rate Change

Let us now consider how this variation in the speed of light affects the rate, i.e. the measurement of time, of a moving clock. If such a clock relies on the sending and receiving of electromagnetic signals through the medium in the FFR, then we propose that when the clock moves through the FFR the clock will run slower. This seems to be the result from SR, but it is not for the same reason. Our proposal is that the *rate* of clocks and all processes [15] decrease *absolutely* due to motion. In other words, it is not time per se that changes as Einstein proposed in his space-time, but simply *the measuring instruments of time*, i.e. clocks record at a different rate when moving, and this has actually been demonstrated experimentally.

We can illustrate this time rate change by beginning with a simple example of measuring a single unit of time of a lightclock that is moving through the FFR. A unit of time, or pulse is measured by a 2-way flash of light to and from a reflector. From a calculation in the FFR, similar to the one above, the light travels at a resultant velocity of ϕc over a 2-way journey perpendicular to the motion. If the absolute distance travelled is d, and the resultant duration for the pulse for a moving lightclock is p, then $p = 2d/\phi c$. Should the same lightclock have been at rest in the FFR the absolute time of the journey would be

$$p_0 = 2d/c.$$

Then:

$$p/p_0 = \frac{2d}{\phi c} \times \frac{c}{2d} \ or \ p = p_0/\phi.$$

This is the familiar result of Time Dilation put *in SR terms* of a moving body where,

$$t' = t/\phi.$$

However, for *framing measurements in absolute terms*, let t_0 be the number of units per second measured by a clock at rest. By at rest, we mean stationary in the FFR. Then let t be the number of units per second of an identical clock, when the clock is moving. Since t is proportional to the inverse of p, and since $p = p_0/\phi$, it follows that the resulting time would be

$$t = \phi t_0$$

This is the formula proposed for Time Rate Change, and is demonstrated by experiment where moving clocks and processes will run slower by the factor ϕ, than when they were stationary.

However, this is not the *slowing* of time. Nor is it time dilation in relativistic terms, i.e. that time itself is something that changes. *Time itself is not changed by motion*. It is simply a consequence of the rate of processes and measuring instruments of time, or actual clocks, that are changed as a result of moving through the system of rest. This causes clocks to record different information.

This leaves the way open not only for *absolute* definitions of time but also for a velocity of light that always *appears* constant since it is measured by clocks that change with motion. Thus an application of this new result would show that Einstein's Clock or Twin paradox vanishes.

Einstein conceded in his Special Theory that a radical rethink of the nature of time was crucial, and indeed SR predicts the slowing of time. However, the comprehensive solution provided in this book is the non-relativistic classic conclusion with clocks that slow and lengths that decrease.

Length Decrease

We now propose that the effect of a body moving through the material FFR is that its length in the direction of travel will decrease. A complete description at the molecular level of a body is highly complex because it involves the mutual interactions of many particles. We therefore take a simple example for illustrative purposes. Suppose that ordinary matter depends on molecular bonding explained in terms of contributions from constituent molecules. We can then consider hypothetical centres in a solid body held in place by quantum molecular bonding of virtual photons that propagate from component particles. Neither Einstein of course, nor Lorentz had the advantage of such knowledge.

Let us suppose that positive ions are found in the hypothetical centres A and C in the figure below, and that the perpendicular repulsive forces from positive ions bond by virtual photons at the speed of light. For the body in motion, bonding between A_1 and C_1 occurs at a velocity that is slower than the speed of light. This will delay the journey of photons, weakening the effect of repulsion and potentially *decreasing* the distance between the centres.

Let us further suppose that the perpendicular attractive force operates differently. This is with negative electrons visiting positions between the ions at regular intervals. The *frequency* of these visits and all other processes will be dictated by the time rate factor ϕ, arising from movement through the FFR. Being multiplied by this factor ϕ, will reduce the electron frequency when a body is in motion, weakening the effect of attraction, and potentially *increasing* the distance between the centres.

The net result with *perpendicular distances* is that the potential decrease and increase cancel and the status quo is maintained.

We must carefully note in the following discussion the importance of whether measurements are made by instruments that are moving or stationary in the FFR.

Thus suppose distance AC is situated perpendicular to the motion, while AB is parallel.

Suppose AC and AB are absolute distances d_0 and l_0 if the body were at rest in the FFR.

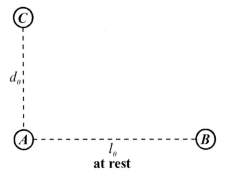

at rest

In motion, suppose distance A_1C_1 is termed d, and distance A_1B_1 is termed l.

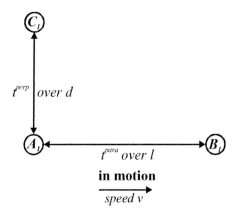

Let t^{perp} represent the resultant duration of a 2-way perpendicular bonding between A_1 and C_1.

Let t^{para} represent the resultant duration of a 2-way parallel bonding between A_1 and B_1.

Because of motion these durations are multiplied by the factor ϕ, for Time Rate Change as $t = \phi t_0$, above.

Each of these measurements is made by instruments at rest in the FFR which will view the figures above as a body moving to the right at velocity v.

Now, photon bonding requires that the duration t^{perp} is determined by the slow velocity ϕc over the 2-way perpendicular distance d. This will weaken the *repulsive* force. Meanwhile, the frequency of electron visits is likewise diminished perpendicularly by the factor ϕ. This in turn will weaken the *attractive* force so that the two forces cancel.

We then see that this duration, t^{perp}, multiplied by ϕ, for electron frequency rate change, takes place in such a way that the status quo of perpendicular forces is conserved where

$$t^{perp} = \phi \left(\frac{d}{\phi c} + \frac{d}{\phi c} \right) = \frac{2d}{c}.$$

While the same frequency rate change is also applied to the 2-way journeys, the duration t^{para}, of parallel repulsive photons that bond between ions at velocities $c+v$ and $c-v$, increases as

$$t^{para} = \phi \left(\frac{l}{c-v} + \frac{l}{c+v} \right) = \phi \left(\frac{2lc}{c^2 - v^2} \right).$$

Since $\phi^2 = \dfrac{c^2 - v^2}{c^2}$ we can write

$$t^{para} = \phi \frac{2l}{\phi^2 c} \text{ or } \frac{2l}{\phi c}.$$

Even though both equations above have the same frequency rate change, repulsive photons from positive ions now run slower. They are therefore weaker at the decreased speed of ϕc, when parallel to v. This causes physical lengths to contract.

Combining the two equations as a ratio demonstrates this conclusively where

$$\frac{t^{perp}}{t^{para}} = \frac{2d}{c} \times \frac{\phi c}{2l} = \phi d / l$$

It is here that we notice a similar ratio of times for the 2-way journey of light between a source and reflector that occurs in such experiments that Michelson and Morley conducted to try to detect an ether. From these experiments there is consistent support for the fact that this ratio is a constant. At the advent of SR this seemed to indicate that there was either no ether, no motion, or that motion in the ether could not be detected and should be ignored.

However, we propose that the instruments of moving bodies as such are merely unaware of this ratio. This is because we have arrived at this ratio from a perspective, not only from an FFR, but also on the assumption that parallel repulsive virtual quantum photons in a rigid body that is moving in an FFR travel between molecules at a slower speed.

On this basis, we now show that the constancy of this ratio is interpreted in a different way from SR.

If $t^{perp} / t^{para} = K$ (a constant) then lengths l of bodies in motion will decrease as

$$l = \phi d / K$$

Taking a particular case at rest in the FFR where $v = 0$, this will give $\phi = 1$, $d = d_0$, $l = l_0$, and $K = d_0 / l_0$. For bodies in motion we can therefore also write

$$\phi d / l = d_0 / l_0$$

Since forces in the parallel direction only seem to be involved where a body is in motion, the expression $d = d_0$ also applies. By substituting d for d_0 in the equation above, lengths l, will be found to decrease as

$$l = \phi l_0$$

This result now seems to conform to SR, but is in effect entirely different. The implication here is that when a body moves in the FFR, its motion is concealed from view by the actual decrease in physical lengths. Therefore, we can conclude that since velocities of perpendicular and parallel journeys of bonding photons vary by the factor ϕ, parallel lengths of physical objects will also vary by the same factor with respect to each other. This ensures that the ratio of time rates of the journeys remain constant as all experiments show.

Any length in motion through the FFR undergoes a contraction not normally observed because the measuring instruments contract correspondingly. Thus, the distance appears unchanged. In the MM experiment this would compensate exactly for the expected difference in the velocity of light in the two directions at right angles. The ratio of the velocities would thus appear to be unity.

This proposal, of course, is open to further examination. However, it does demonstrate a basis on which we can return to absolute measurements at rest in the universe, and offer explanations for problems accompanying SR, such as we will now see in Simultaneity.

6

Simultaneity

Let us therefore examine Einstein's definition of Simultaneity more closely based on our discussion in terms of time.

Einstein stipulates as shown on page 34 ff. that

> *"The two clocks are synchronous by definition if*
>
> $$t_B - t_A = t'_A - t_B$$ *"*

and that

> *"Based on experience, we further stipulate that the quantity*
>
> $$\frac{2\overline{AB}}{t'_A - t_A} = c$$
>
> *be a universal constant (the velocity of light in empty space)."*

If we simplify this second equation where $t_A = 0$, and let distance $2AB = 2l_0$, Einstein's sum of times for the 2-way passage of light between A and B, t'_A, can be written as

$$t'_A = 2l_0 / c.$$

Einstein implied from this that the times for the outward and return journeys must be the same, which disallows an FFR unless the system is *"a rest system"*. Moreover, Einstein's definition of Simultaneity remains ambiguous as practical knowledge of the value of B's clock t_B, is denied, and his theoretical conclusion is not free of contradictions since it is maintained without means of proof. However, let us now consider this equation viewed from the absolute position of the FFR.

Suppose the system of AB is *not* seen to be *"a rest system"* in Einstein's terms, but a system travelling 'east' at speed v, with respect to the FFR in which light travels at speed c. How do we synchronise A and B time, t_A and t_B, from an absolute position?

Let us use 2-way light signals in a moving system monitored by instruments at rest in the FFR.

west $\boxed{A}$ $\xleftarrow{\quad l = \phi l_0 \quad}$ $\boxed{B}$ east
$$\xrightarrow{\quad v \quad}$$

Since the duration of the sum of times for the 2-way journey parallel to v on page 46 was $t^{para} = 2l / \phi c$, can we now match this expression with Einstein's time embodying his absolute term, t'_A?

Now, since length AB decreases with motion, as $l = \phi l_0$, page 48, we can substitute the term l, for ϕl_0, so that the expression $t^{para} = 2l / \phi c$, above, becomes $t^{para} = 2\phi l_0 / \phi c$. When simplified we then have

$$t^{para} = 2l_0 / c.$$

Next, we find on page 51 that since $2l_0/c$ also equals t'_A, we can forego the term t^{para}, and embody t'_A instead, so that

$$t'_A = 2l_0/c .$$

We now see that the overall time t'_A of our 2-way passage of light in a moving object is still the same that Einstein stipulated, *even though it does not originate from his "rest system"*. Furthermore, the times for the two 1-way journeys of light, A to B and B to A, i.e. $2\phi l_0/(c+v)$ and $2\phi l_0/(c-v)$, are different, which Einstein completely disallowed. Extraordinarily, Einstein's own result masks the fact that the 1-way time and speed of light for AB *can* be different.

Note. *We can only ever <u>observe</u> the 2-way overall results of the passage of light, and <u>that</u> is the root of the problem for Relativity Theory.*

7

The Speed of Light

Let us now show why, as has been demonstrated by experiments, the speed of light is always found to be the same numerical value c, masking the fact that its speed varies for 1-way travel in moving objects.

In this discussion we must be careful to note that instruments at rest in the FFR record measurements that are absolute[16] and that instruments moving with the body AB record measurements that are not absolute.

$$A \underline{\hspace{1cm} \phi l_0 \hspace{1cm}} B$$
$$\longrightarrow v$$

Suppose AB is moving at speed **v** while light is transmitted from A to B and reflected back to A. The light travels parallel to **v** at speed **c** in the FFR. Due to motion it is received at B at speed **c** – **v** and at A at speed **c** + **v**.

First, let instruments that are stationary in the FFR determine the speed of light for AB. Distance AB is measured by instruments stationary in the FFR as contracted length $l = \phi l_0$. The absolute duration t_0, for the 2-way parallel beam of light reflected over AB will then be timed by a clock stationary in the FFR.

The total time t_0, for the 2-way parallel beam of light that travels from A to B and back at different speeds over shortened distance AB will then be equal to

$$\frac{\phi l_0}{c - v} + \frac{\phi l_0}{c + v}.$$

Adding the two times gives

$$\frac{2\phi l_0}{c^2 - v^2}.$$

Simplifying by extracting ϕ^2, where

$$\phi^2 = \frac{c^2 - v^2}{c^2},$$

gives

$$\frac{2\phi l_0}{c} \times \frac{c_2}{c^2 - v^2},$$

or

$$\frac{2\phi l_0}{\phi^2 c}.$$

Simplifying again gives us the time

$$\frac{2l_0}{\phi c}.$$

The units of time AB are thus increased because the *average* speed of light for the 2-way journey is slow at ϕc, and takes longer.

However, since AB is moving, this expression of time for AB, which is now

$$t_0 = 2l_0 / \phi c,$$

should be multiplied by ϕ, for time rate change so that it becomes $\phi \times (2l_0 / \phi c)$, or

$$2l_0 / c.$$

This gives the value of the time seen from the FFR but measured by a clock <u>moving with AB</u> as

$$t^{AB} = 2l_0 / c.$$

Next, instruments travelling with AB will be unaware of any movement through the FFR, and will measure the contracted length as l, which the FFR sees as being ϕl_0. However, rulers moving with AB as well as the lengths being measured contract in the same ratio. Then instruments moving with AB will obtain the *value* for the length AB as

$$\phi l_0^{AB} = \phi l_0,$$

and for the distance for the 2-way journey of light A to B and back as

$$2l_0^{AB} = 2l_0.$$

So, according to the units of length and time on the measuring instruments that are moving, the value of the 'average' speed of light for the 2-way travel (total distance over total time) is $2l_0 \div 2l_0 / c = c$, or

$$2l_0{}^{AB} / t^{AB} = c.$$

The constant *numerically similar* value of c is derived here by instruments moving with AB from units of length and time that are affected by length decrease and time rate change. Thus, although the speeds ($c-v$ and $c+v$) of 1-way journeys of light between A and B are different, the <u>overall</u> *average* speed is constant for any double journey. Without considering any reciprocal view of the FFR, this is the result that experiments will always show.

We stress again this important observation: the speed of light averaged over a 2-way journey to a reflector and back is found to have the same *value* that we denote by c, whatever the speed of the moving instruments. This is because the units of the measurements of time and length change with the motion, when compared with absolute measurements made from instruments stationary in the FFR. The units of time are thus longer as t^{AB}, and the units of length are shorter as $l_0{}^{AB}$, but this is not perceived by the instruments in motion. The calculation nevertheless produces the same value for the speed of light.

Reciprocal view of the FFR

We comment on this phenomenon, leaving further consideration for future publications. Relativistic Reciprocity means that any system whether moving or not considers itself at rest, and deduces values for all other bodies from this 'rest system'. Any other body may also consider itself at rest and deduce values for other bodies likewise. Reciprocity in the FFR is similar to SR but allowance must be made for FFR changes in the Galilean sense.

Addition of Velocities

When considering Addition of Velocities this is assessed in Newtonian terms. If a disturbance is made in the FFR, radiation travels in opposite directions at the combined speed $2c$[16]. Additions and subtractions of velocities in other situations follow likewise.

We would refer again briefly here to the subtle elegance of the Lorentz Transformations[17], and suggest that this *elegance* is beguiling and is *a root of the problems in SR*. We submit therefore, that Lorentz's equations should be rejected.

8

Conclusions

We have proposed that physics return to the consideration of a Fixed Frame of Reference in absolute space, and have shown how Special Relativity is incompatible with such a model. Einstein's suppositions were inexact when he assumed that an FFR could be ignored. It is intriguing that this fact has been obscured for over a century. This is because the 2-way 'average' speed of light travelling between a source and reflector agrees with the suppositions of his theory. This is advanced while hiding the inequality of the 1-way journeys of the light in a body moving in an FFR.

In arguing these points of making a variable speed of light a distinct possibility, we have raised important new perspectives beyond standard theory which seem close to relativistic concepts, but are so different as to imply significant redefinition. By this we imply the existence of a form of cosmic plasma in space that not only makes a variable speed of light a distinct possibility but also opens the way to further studies beyond standard theory.

If the proposals in this book now present a logical breakthrough beyond Special Relativity, which we believe they do, we can begin to think in terms of the further implications in order to consider what new information a fixed plasma or matrix might provide. This may be deduced from the cosmic material of which the FFR might have been made.

Table of issues affected by increase in velocity

Issue	Relativity Theory	Our Perceptions
Speed of Light	Einstein assumes this constant in any direction.	We say constancy is only in *averaged* two way travel.
Time	Einstein says *time* changes.	We say *clocks in motion* record time differently due to their interaction with the FFR.
Length	Einstein says *length* changes.	We say *actual physical material and rulers* change .
Simultaneity	Einstein assumes the time for the outward and return journey of light *is the same.*	We say the time for the outward and return journeys of light *can be different* and this permits a FFR.
Mass	Einstein says *mass* increases.	We say mass increases but *not for the same reason* (not stated above).
Absolutes	Einstein does not refute.	We say *there are absolutes* of mass, time and space.
Medium of the FFR	Einstein *does not deny* its existence.	We say *it does exist* but may not be detectable for the reasons stated.

9

Further Implications

Cosmology in a Fixed Frame of Reference

Résumé

At the beginning of the book we highlighted how history was littered with failed attempts to answer the basic question 'How does light work?'

We saw how the concept of a light-bearing ether foundered when experiments tried to detect it. This culminated in Einstein's Theory of Special Relativity that ignored it, but in doing so a new set of problems arose. However, although we found our ability to bypass Relativity Theory extremely challenging, it was one of the most important results of our study. We therefore proceeded in the context of a matrix or Fixed Frame of Reference (FFR) which naturally led to further implications for the universe that we then explored.

A variable speed of light

Our first thoughts were drawn towards devising a model, still in early speculative stages, for resolving questions in a different way. A variable speed of light made the existence of a cosmic matrix in absolute space a distinct possibility. Thus, should this theory prove a successful step beyond Relativity Theory and the study of the geometry of the universe embracing an absolute rest position be re-opened, we saw that the FFR promised an attractive future. Such a model already in considerable detail might provide suitable material for a further study.

Space

In short, the FFR embraces a model that embodies the fixing of an absolute unchangeable component of quantised free space neither affecting nor affected by the dynamic changes occurring in its material parts. This solution then becomes analogous to a computer screen, having a Euclidean lattice partitioned into small interstices or cells $\approx 10^{-17}$m, endowed with certain physical properties. These cells remain unaltered neither aiding nor hindering the action, though their presence is essential for the perception of the software.

It is then necessary to assume the presence of a more active ingredient for the software—a cosmic plasma—taking on a dynamic role in the motions and phenomena of the universe. Briefly, this ingredient involves two digital fluids, which move but not like ordinary fluids. In more precise detail, they comprise the maximum of two opposite *quanta*, one from each fluid coexisting per cell with their magnitude close to Planck's constant $\approx h$, and having options of movement into adjacent cells. Discrete Motion Rules then determine quanta densities and all movement of the 2-fluids in time-steps, its granularity overcoming the singularity problem. Interestingly, the completed fabric of the FFR would have been far too intricate to have evolved. It had to have been made.

Matter

Any material ether or matrix has always been hampered with one particular problem. That is, if signals travel through it at the speed at which we suppose, the material of which it is made must possess immense tensile strength. This has attendant problems of the passage of bodies through it.

In our model however, particles, or what we call electrons, protons etc. are not 'solid' in the usual sense. They are in fact places in the matrix where the density of one or other of the 2-fluids is *less* than the surrounding 'vacuum' . Particles are thus waves or *wavehollows* in the density of the fluids. One could picture them in the matrix as one would a negative photograph with forces between bodies still behaving in the same way, but dependent on the matrix for action at a distance. As the hollows travel through the matrix or FFR, quanta flow through the hollows in the opposite direction. 'Solid objects' are thus not inhibited while they pursue their free passage through it [18].

Origins

Since no scheme that presupposes the origin of the universe can ever be other than hypothetical, it is fair to contend that an FFR should not be ignored. The following account is therefore proposed as a possible past event.

Suppose that a uniform 100% original density of the 2-fluids experienced a rapid inaugural attenuation at a point in its history. Suppose also that this attenuation of fluid densities was extended to the perimeter of the universe. Let us further suppose that the rapid velocity of gravitational propagation can be taken into account [19], and that the efficiency of the speed of light is directly proportional to the density of fluids (similar to sound in water)[16]. Then light could have travelled from newly formed objects over large distances in a matter of days and slowed down later as the attenuation settled into a steady state.

Cosmic Microwave Background

The internal forces of these fluids would have ensured that they formed into a large concave perimeter surface seen, as it were, from inside the universe. Now, we know from experiment that a concave surface acts as a *perfect blackbody reflector* for scattering incident radiation. Such a blackbody reflector could thus have been scattering incident radiation throughout the FFR since then. Such radiation may now be observable on earth in the form of the newly discovered Cosmic Microwave Background (CMB). Research into this has shown more recently that the earth is circling *through* the CMB at 600km/sec round our galaxy, the Milky Way. Our model presumes that this velocity is not merely through the CMB, but could confirm the velocity of the earth with respect to the absolute rest position of the FFR.

Gravitation

Concerning the force of gravity, Newton wondered about it three centuries ago. Einstein's proposal that matter distorts 'space-time' has left us with the question why gravity is still such a profound mystery. Simply put, gravitation in our theory is found inversely proportional to the density of the 2-fluids [20]. That is, the greater the hollow the greater the potential [20]. Thus, being wavehollows, particles of matter are gravitational sinks in the 2-fluids that act, as we would suppose. In other words, gravitation occurs where the 2-fluids neutralise each other. The exception is where weak molecular bonding replaces gravitational attraction at a very close range sometimes referred to as the Casimir force [21], (see 'Experiments', page 69 and 'References and Notes', page 71).

On a large scale, the attenuation of fluid densities would have ended in a gradient most steeply curved near the perimeter of the universe. Gravitational potential there would then be at its most intense, but *outwards*.

Now, gravitation from the combined matter of the whole universe, left on its own, would draw all matter *inwards* and collapse it towards the centre of the universe. Clearly, this is not happening. Standard theory overcomes this problem by asserting that the universe is expanding. However, in this model, the universe could be so balanced by the two opposing outward and inward gravitational potentials that it maintains a steady state of repose in what we might call a non-expanding universe.

There is one further point on gravitation concerning the transfer efficiency or speed of light, it being directly proportional to the density of fluids. Taking an individual photon, the speed of its near and far side, if we can visualise such a picture, could be unequally biased when crossing a fluid gradient. As has already been observed from objects behind massive gravitational sinks such as the sun, this could be the reason why these photons are seen to bend round such objects. This of course would be for a different reason to that advanced by General Relativity.

Red Shift

'Red or Doppler Shift' is normally described as the lengthening of the wavelengths of light into the red end of the spectrum originating from objects that are receding from an observer. Now, when sound waves travel through fog, they appear dampened. Likewise, light being directly dependent upon the fluid densities, would propagate faster and more efficiently in higher fluid densities and slower and more scattered through low densities.

Now, because fluids are attenuated in our model, their densities decrease towards the perimeter of the universe. Suppose our earth was near the centre, light would gather pace as it approached us. This increase in the speed of light could be the reason we give for the red shift observed from distant objects and not that of their recession.

That said, this increase in the speed of light from distant objects would have accelerated most rapidly in the steeper attenuation gradient of fluid densities discussed above, nearest the perimeter of the universe and be observed in the red shifts. This would appear to Standard Theory however, as though their *recession* was accelerating. Such a strange phenomenon of apparent acceleration of recession of these objects recently discovered, is being explained by the introduction of a mysterious dark energy pulling the objects outwards [22].

Age and Extent of the Universe

It is clear that this model departs from the idea of red shifts that suppose an expanding universe originating in a Big Bang, and leaves both as open questions. However, from the perspective of our proposals, we could indeed be seeing light from distant objects being red shifted because of its increase in speed towards us. Therefore, the idea of the red shift being caused by an expanding universe may be convincing us wrongly that these objects are much older and further away than they actually are.

Experiments

We propose that the future implications above may prompt a visit to a number of experiments.

In short, these could possibly:

- Reveal a change in the velocity of light passing through a discharge or Faraday Cage thereby confirming a different interpretation for the red shift of distant starlight.

- Offer an alternative explanation for the CMB (Cosmic Microwave Background) by reassessing the nature of its wavelengths.

- Demystify the incompatibility of relativity theory and the quantum phenomenon through a fine-tuned double slit experiment.

- Test a current-carrying vessel using charged particles in a visible low temperature plasma so as to portray a fresh reassessment of our understanding of the fundamental principles behind electromagnetism and electromagnetic radiation. This experiment, already in progress, might furnish an alternative experimental fusion reactor.

- Measure the force between closely positioned plates when surfaced with chemicals of different charge elements to demonstrate that the Casimir force is reliant merely upon molecular qualities.

References and Notes

1. Edited and recently reprinted in Stachel, John, *Einstein's Miraculous Year*, Princeton University Press, pp.123–160, 1998.

2. A useful summary of this experiment is found in French, A. P., *Special Relativity*, Massachusetts Institute of Technology, pp.51–56, 1968.

3. These problems became such classic difficulties that scientists began to ignore or deny the existence of an ether. Whether or not it existed ceased to be an issue when the principles of relativity were conceived and attention was diverted from further investigations to detect it. Nevertheless, it seems it can still resolve problems that relativity has brought. These are those that occur in the meaning and measurement of time, its difficulties with quantum theory, electrodynamics, singularities, the red shift of light and the origin and extent of the universe.

4. *Einstein's Miraculous Year*, p124.

5. *Special Relativity*, p93.

6. *Einstein's Miraculous Year*, p124.

7. Absolute rest is the state in space from which the velocities of all bodies in the universe are assessed whether detectable or not.

8. *Special Relativity*, p80.

9. *Einstein's Miraculous Year*, p126.

10. For instance, Bergmann, Peter, *McGraw-Hill Multimedia Encyclopaedia of Science and Technology*, 2000. The section on 'Space-time' gives a useful description.

> "In accordance with the Lorentz Transformations, both the time interval and the spatial distance between two events are relative quantities, depending on the state of motion of the observer who carries out the measurements. However, a new absolute quantity takes the place of the two former quantities. It is known as the invariant, or proper, *space-time* interval t and is defined [below], where τ is the ordinary time interval,
>
> $$\tau^2 = T - \frac{1}{c^2} R^2,$$
>
> R the distance between the two events, and c the speed of light in empty space. Whereas T and R are different for different observers, t has the same value."

Conventionally, in terms of absolute definitions, time is measured in days, which can be subdivided into hours, minutes and seconds. The absolute measure of time until the 1960s is that a day is measured by one rotation of the earth as observed through the position of the sun. On the earth, clocks are calibrated to this. If a clock moves and its rate of recording changes, it has ceased to measure time correctly. If however, someone defines time according to its rate of recording, then time becomes a phenomenon of relativity and so is redefined.

11. *Einstein's Miraculous Year*, p127.

12. Here we note that 'time dilation' is a relativistic term of SR. Later we shall return to the argument that this is misleading because time per se does not change. It is the time rate in the measuring instruments such as clocks that changes. For this reason and because we propose a return to absolute measurements we will use the term 'time rate change' instead of 'time dilation', together with time rate factor ϕ, in equation $t = \phi t_0$. We propose that this affects all processes.

13. For similar reasons in note 12 above, we will use the term 'length decrease', with equation $l = \phi l_0$. Though this may seem pedantic, we are concerned to avoid the use of relativistic terms.

14. To help understand this important point—a slow velocity of light—we can illustrate this concept with a simple example. Suppose a child's ball rolls from side to side in the cabin of a ship steaming through the water at velocity v. In our diagram, the ball has a speed of its own over perpendicular distance A_1C_1 and back of

$$2 \times \sqrt{c^2 - v^2}.$$

However, to instruments on a stationary barge nearby, the ball traces an apparent zigzag over AC_1 and back. Since the completed journeys take the same time as observed from the two perspectives, but over different distances, this must result in different speed measurements. This is relative motion in the normal Newtonian sense.

Now, suppose we consider light. The only difference is that photons travel in the medium at a fixed maximum speed of c. Thus, because the two photon-journeys likewise take the same time, the speed over the perpendicular distance A_1C_1 will *appear from the perspective of the FFR* to be slower at ϕc. Neither the child nor the solid body, of course, will notice any difference in their own speeds, as we shall show later.

15. We recognise that there are various kinds of timing mechanisms, e.g. atomic clocks and pendulum clocks. While agreeing that the slowing of clocks is a physical fact that has been tested, it remains to be seen if *all* timing mechanisms and processes run slow, at the same rate. Interestingly, if they do not, this would enable us to detect motion through the FFR. However, here we are simply taking the example of a light clock for illustrative purposes. In any event, one form of timing device, e.g. an atomic clock or lightclock would be used as the datum for calibrating all clocks in a moving system. Any difference in slowing for a variety of types of clocks would thereby be masked.

16. Based on the assumption that such measurements can be accurately made, absolute measurements, i.e. t_0 and l_0, are those apparent to instruments presumed to be at the absolute rest position fixed with respect to the unchangeable component (Space; page 64). However, we propose that the actual speed of light depends on fluid densities and their efficiency in carrying light (similar to light or sound in water).

While we realise that such concepts are hypothetical, our argument is nonetheless based on this hypothesis. Other bodies seen to be moving, say AB, also have length and time measured by instruments moving with AB and deemed to have absolute values l_0^A, and t_0^A. They are unaware of their motion with respect to the FFR and do not agree with instruments already at rest in the FFR. Resulting measurements by instruments at rest in the FFR are those measurements based on the reaction of a body assumed to be moving in the FFR, i.e. $t = \phi t_0$, and $l = \phi l_0$. We need to distinguish these carefully, since instruments that are moving change when in motion.

17. Refer to French, A. P., *Special Relativity*, p80.

18. When a particle or body accelerates, inertia arises from a potential barrier encountered in the FFR as soon as there is a demand for change in speed or direction. The response to such a change is not only directly proportional to the size of a particle or body, but is also not instantaneous, spreading through the

particle at c^2, and confined to discrete time-steps by the Motion Rules.

An interesting question posed by Lorentz asks,

> "Is it conceivable that a moving body can experience a resistance to acceleration unless there is an ether to provide the resistance?"

This very phenomenon was cited by him in support of his theory before Einstein's Paper on relativity appeared. Refer to *Proc. Acad. Sci. Amsterdam 1904* by H. A. Lorentz, reprinted in *The Principle of Relativity* by Einstein and Others (Methuen 1923).

19. Refer to van Flandern in:
<http://www.ldolphin.org/vanFlandern/gravityspeed.html> 'The Speed of Gravity – What the Experiments Say' (accessed 8 December 2005). The speed of gravity is calculated to be greater than $\approx 2 \times 10^{10} c$, or equal to 60,000,000,000,000,000km/s. It is unlikely therefore, that current experiments aimed at searching for gravitational waves from astrophysical sources will be successful.

20. The gravitational potential of particles according to this model is due to a systematic anomaly in the 2-fluids and becomes most evident when the charge element of particles is neutralised in molecules. This is most commonly experienced where particles cluster together.

21. Our model attributes the strange Casimir force that draws smooth plates together, to the predominance of intermolecular or weak van der Waals-like bonding where charges are no longer neutralised at very close range (see experiment).

22. Refer to *The Supernova Cosmology Project* by Professor Saul Perlmutter, Astrophysics Experiment 1998 Group Site:

    <http://supernova.lbl.gov/~saul/home.html> (accessed 8 December 2005).

Index

Index

81

Printed in the United States
41971LVS00001B/358-414